NED and the GENERAL

A Lesson About Deployment

by
Ron Madison

Illustrations by
David Covolo

ISBN 1-887206-24-8 H/C
ISBN 1-887206-25-6 PBC

Printed in the U. S. A.

First printing, 2004

NED and the GENERAL

A Lesson About Deployment

Contents

Jim's Story

Ned's friend Jim was really sad.
Never had he looked this bad.

"Dad is leaving, going away.
When he'll be back, he wouldn't say.

"He's going real far, a place called Iraq.
I'm scared to death he'll never come back.

"I hate the Army! They're mean. They're bad.
Why don't they take someone else's dad?"

What could Ned say? What could he do?
How could he help get Jim through?

Ned gave him a hug. They had a good cry.
Ned said he'd help. At least he would try.

Alex's Story

The kids were dressed in old Polish style,
and Polish music played all the while.

It was cool to watch as they danced and spun,
and Alex was there, having great fun.

His mouth wore a smile, his step was spry,
yet sadness filled Alex's eye.

His mom left home a year ago.
Alex told Ned he missed her so.

"I tell myself she'll just be away
for only two weeks. That's what I say.

"That's how I cope. That's how I get by.
It builds up my courage. I try not to cry.

"But I cry every night, it gives me the creeps,
'cause honestly, Ned, it's a long two weeks!"

Vicki's Story

Alex's sister, from all Ned could tell,
seemed to be taking it all very well.

He knew his friend was hurting inside,
but she never let on. She kept her pride.

"I keep myself busy all summer long,
with sports and music to help me along.

"That's how I cope, while Mom is away.
That's how I get by, day after day.

"I'm happy that summer is over at last.
I find that school helps make time pass.

"When Mom comes home, we all can renew
the family life that we once knew."

Ned felt her fear and said with a groan,
"What if your Mom doesn't come home?"

She thought for a while, then let out a sigh,
"I'm scared to death that Mom might die.

"And then I think how bad it would be,
if Dad told Mom something happened to me."

J.P.'s Story

"When Dad went away, I was too young to know
the reason why he had to go.

"I picked up a bag, filled it with stuff,
just some things I thought were enough.

"I'd find him somehow, that much I knew.
I only wanted a hug or two.

"I was out the door and down the street.
Then I got scared. My heart skipped a beat.

"I went back home. Yet I dreamed every night
that Dad was home and held me tight.

"For a long, long time I felt alone.
Then, at last, my Dad came home.

"He was so much different than I recall.
Not like my Dad. No, not at all!

"I ran to my room. I felt so bad.
How could I tell he was really my Dad?

"I crept downstairs to where he sat
with a strange, sad look. I remember that.

"I jumped on his lap. He squeezed me tight.
I'll feel that hug for the rest of my life!"

Kathy's Story

"You want to know how I really feel?
Dad's being gone is no big deal.

"It's part of his job. It's what he must do,
whether school or camp or overseas, too.

"He's gone a lot. We're used to it now.
We care for ourselves. We had to learn how.

"The TV stays off. It would make us sad,
just hoping to catch a glimpse of Dad.

"When you're regular Army, folks come through.
At your base or school, they do help you.

"Dad's a pro. I'm proud of him.
He'll be home, but not till we win!"

Mrs. Arcurio's Class

As class began, Mrs. Arcurio read
the news from Iraq. And then she said,

"I'd like to know if any of you
have a Mom or Dad over there, too."

Ned looked at Jim, who said not a word.
No one spoke. Not a sound was heard.

"Let's just pretend," she went on to ask,
"it happened to you. How would you act?"

"I'd tell no one. Can't you see,
it's none of their business what happens to me."

That was Rosa. They all felt the same.
So teacher went on with her "what-if" game.

"How would you feel if it happened to you?
How would you act? What would you do?"

"I'd have trouble with my grades."
..."I wouldn't study, anyways."

"I'd feel lonely!"..."I'd feel sad!"
"I'd feel blue!"..."I'd be mad!"

"I'd be so angry," Rosa then said,
"I'd punch someone, right in the head!"

Jim was surprised that they all knew
what he himself was going through.

Teacher asked, "What if you knew
a friend like that. What would you do?"

"I'd tell my friend I understood."
"I'd give her a hug so she'd feel good."

"I'd let him talk, if he wanted to.
It often helps to talk things through."

"I'd want my friend to be aware
that I want to help. I really care."

Jim was moved. He wished he could
tell them all. Some day he would.

He told his teacher later on
about his Dad, how he was gone.

"So that's what's wrong. Now I know.
I should have asked you long ago."

Jim hung his head. He wasn't mad,
but softly said, "I wish you had!"

Grandpa John

Ned told Johnny how Jim felt.
"Is there any way we can help?"

Johnny said, "You ought to meet
my Grandpa John. He's really neat.

"When I grow up I want to be
just like him. You wait and see.

"He's lots of fun. He likes to play,
was quite an athlete in his day.

"There's lots of things he still can do,
especially when I ask him to.

"When I beat him in a go-cart race,
a surly grin fills his face.

"He once showed me his general's hat,
and on my head it proudly sat.

"I said to him, 'It's fun to be
a three-star general. That's for me!'

"Grandpa frowned and took the hat,
'It's not as simple as all that.

'The fun, the perks, the privilege, too,
that go with the job are great, it's true.

'But the toughest thing I had to do
I've never ever shared with you.

'To decide just how and when and where
to send my troops, and get them there

to protect the things that we love best,
so those brave few might save the rest.

'My troops were folks with children too,
boys and girls, just like you.

'And what I sought far and above,
was to bring them home to those they love.'"

The General's Story

Ned and his friends were in town one day.
They saw the General on the way.

He was glad to see them, invited them in,
kissed his grandson and said with a grin,

"What brings you here on this nice day?"
It was Ned who gathered the courage to say,

"Would you tell us what we should know.
Why kids' parents have to go

far, far away to fight a war?
What's the reason? What's it for?"

The General thought and then he said,
"That's quite a question. I hear you, Ned.

"It's tough when Dad or Mom is gone.
It's tough to feel so much alone.

"But remember why they chose to go.
It's because they really love you so.

"They want to keep you safe and free,
a better world for you and me.

"You'll miss them while they are away.
And if you cry, that's OK.

"And please don't think you have to keep
your hurt and fear way down deep.

"Let it out. Let people know.
You'll like the love that they will show.

"It'll ease the hurt that now haunts you
and give you strength to see it through.

"Moms and Dads way over there,
need to know you really care.

"There's a job to do that must be done.
It's theirs to do, every one.

"Be proud of them for what they do,
as proud of them as they of you."

USA

Jim's New Role

Ned had learned a great deal
about these kids, and how they feel.

With all he knew, he thought he would
let Jim know he understood.

But Ned found Jim no longer sad.
Jim learned too and wasn't mad.

He said to Ned, "Since Dad's been gone,
I'm man of the house. I must be strong.

"I'll help my Mom as best I can.
That's how I'll cope. That's my plan.

"If I do that well, and keep on track,
how proud he'll be, when he comes back."

Professional Commentary

As a result of a growing public awareness of the problems of deployment, more and more families who have a parent deployed are coming to me for help.

When children are faced with the deployment of a parent, their world, as they know it, is turned upside down. The family unit and daily family functioning will never be the same. Whether or not it is identified as such, children (and other family members) will experience feelings of grief and loss for the family they knew. When one member is removed for an extended period of time, relationships are renegotiated and roles are reassigned. Some of this change occurs in obvious ways, but much of it is subtle and can impact children deeply.

Responding to grief and loss is unique for each and every person. There is no time frame or cookie-cutter response. Each person's framework affects his or her response. Culture, religion, family models and gender play significant roles in a grief response. In the United States today, when raising sons and daughters, we can inadvertently give them messages on how to deal with sadness and loss. When girls are told it is "okay to cry" and boys are told "to be a man," we may be limiting how they express themselves.

When a parent returns home, there is a definitive period of readjustment for all family members. This "new" family unit will establish itself within the confines of the former structure. This takes time. If needed, professional help should be sought for the readjustment phase.

It is so essential to take time to talk and share feelings and information with children on a regular basis. Most importantly, never assume you know how they are feeling; keep asking.

Helping children understand a purpose for deployment, as *Ned and the General* does, will support them greatly in their response. Notifying friends, school personnel and activity coordinators (such as coaches) will provide continued support for children.

Let me introduce myself. I am a counselor/psychotherapist in private practice with advanced training in grief and loss and trauma/crisis situations in the family. In my practice, I have seen many children and adults who are experiencing profound grief and loss in their lives. It is a multi-faceted dilemma.

Ned and the General is an excellent reference for families involved with deployment and with many similar crisis situations. As Dr. Ron says, "These stories specifically deal with the deployment of a parent, but it is obvious that the same emotions apply to a number of other family situations."

Ellie Neveling, RN, MEd
Counselor

Author's Note

Research for this project included interviews with schoolchildren and parents who have had or are now experiencing the hardships of deployment. The stories included here are based on those interviews as well as interviews with several military people. I am particularly grateful for the advice I received from professionals active in counseling families in crisis.

I also visited several third grade classrooms. None of the children said (or would admit) they had a parent deployed. Yet I was amazed by how well the children understood how such a classmate might feel. Their comments echoed what I had previously heard during my interviews and what was suggested by professional counselors. When their teachers asked what the students would do to help such a child, we were pleasantly surprised to learn how much they would want to help and just how they might go about it. I have captured their thoughts in the chapter, "Mrs. Arcurio's Class."

With the exception of the two stories about Jim, the children's stories are real. These are their stories; I merely put them to rhyme. "Jim's Story" is not one child's story; it represents how all the children felt. "Jim's New Role" is not a story I heard from any of the children; I created it to indicate what we, as adults, would like the children to believe.

The fact of the matter is that the children's stories speak for themselves. They are far more effective than anything I might create as an author.

Conventional wisdom dictated that the adult mentor in the book should be someone the children might recognize and easily relate to, such as a sergeant or a company commander. I chose instead to provide the children the opportunity of meeting a real general. Grandpa John in real life is a family man in the true sense, loved by his children and grandchildren. That, plus his outstanding military career, makes him the ideal mentor I wanted.

Although I have written *Ned and the General* for children, I have never considered children to be my sole audience. I am also writing to parents, grandparents, teachers –and the generals. All of them need to know the reality of how these children feel.

These stories deal specifically with the deployment of a parent, but it is obvious that the same emotions apply to a number of other family situations.

Acknowledgements

I would like to thank those individuals whose stories I used in this book and whose advice helped me to write it.

I particularly want to thank John Conaway, Lieutenant General, U. S. Air Force (Ret), former Chief of the National Guard, who was the role model for "The General's Story." I want to thank him not only for his support, but also for sharing his family with me. Though I have long considered him a friend, to write his story I had to get to know him as a father and grandfather, and I did that through his daughter, sons and grandsons. My thanks to Ellen Williams, Daniel and David Conaway, and grandsons: Joey, Sam, Matt, Danny, Michael and Johnny. David is a Commander in the U. S. Navy (Ret) and Michael is in the U. S. Army ROTC.

I want to thank those families who were willing to share their experiences with me and whose children provided the stories I have used in this book:

Sergeant First Class Marie Hammer, U. S. Army Reserve, her husband David Hammer and their children Alexander, Victoria and Elizabeth
Colonel John Skelley, U. S. Marine Corps Reserves, his wife Joselle and their son J. P.
Robert Simmons, Major, U. S. Marine Corps (Ret), his wife Pat and their daughter Katherine.

I want to thank those third grade students at East Side Elementary School in Johnstown PA who provided me with their insightful thoughts for "Mrs. Arcurio's Class," and their teachers: Amy Arcurio, Stacey Ford and Rose McClelland.

I want to thank Ellie Neveling, Registered Nurse and Master of Education, and Neal J. Palles, Master of Social Work and Licensed Clinical Social Worker, for helping me to better understand the professional aspects of the effects of deployment.

I wish to thank Major Joseph Conrad, Pennsylvania National Guard, for his interest and support of my work.

Finally, I want to thank the many people who shared their experiences and offered their support to help me write this book, including: Joseph A. Columbus, Sergeant, U. S. Marine Corps (Ret), Veteran Affairs, Cambria County, PA; David Harris, Major General, Illinois National Guard (Ret); Tammy Hearn, wife of Staff Sergeant William J. Hearn, U. S. Army, and their son Joshua; Jeffery Marsteller, First Lieutenant, U. S. Army Reserve, his wife Shawn and their children Denee, Hallie and Reagan; Keith Martin, Brigadier General, Pennsylvania National Guard (Ret); Paul E. Neatrour, Colonel, Pennsylvania National Guard (Ret); Kathleen M. Willason, Captain, U. S. Army (Ret).

GAYLORD M2